1

Old Sky is big as big can be.
Because he's so big, you can
never see him all at one time.

Beside him, Father Sun looks very small.

Can you find him?

He's way over there.

At this time of day, he's just a dot.

At this time of day, it's time for us to sleep.

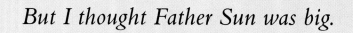

But I thought Father Sun was big.

He is big as big can be.

And he's hot.

He brings each morning to start the day.

Beside him, Mother Earth is very small.

You're standing on her!

She's the one with water and fish.

She's the one with trees and plants and you!

5

But I thought Mother Earth was big.

She is big as big can be.

Even in a jet, I bet you can't see

Mother Earth all in one day.

Beside her, Sister Moon is small.

Sister Moon makes the water go up

and then down again.

7

But I thought Sister Moon was big.

She is big as big can be.

Beside her you are just a little one,

way up there in that tree.

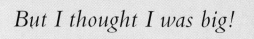

But I thought I was big!

You are big as big can be.

Beside you that snail is very, very small.

If he went as fast as he could,

it would take all day just for him

to get down from the tree.

And so, my friend,
you are not too big or too small.
You are just the way you are.
And that is good!